This Bing book belongs to:

....

Copyright © 2022 Acamar Films Ltd

The *Bing* television series is created by Acamar Films and Brown Bag Films and adapted from the original books by Ted Dewan.

Kite (pp.10–17) is based on the original story written by Chris Parker, Lucy Murphy, Mikael Shields and Ted Dewan.
Musical Statues (pp.30–37) is based on the original story written by Philip Bergkvist, Lucy Murphy, Mikael Shields and Ted Dewan.
Voosh! (pp.50–57) is based on the original story written by Kate Henderson, Lucy Murphy, Mikael Shields and An Vrombaut

10 9 8 7 6 5 4 3 2 1

ISBN: 978-0-00-849776-7

First published in the United Kingdom by HarperCollins *Children's Books* in 2022
HarperCollins *Children's Books* is a division of HarperCollins*Publishers* Ltd
1 London Bridge Street
London SE1 9GF

www.harpercollins.co.uk

HarperCollins*Publishers*,
1st Floor, Watermarque Building, Ringsend Road
Dublin 4, Ireland

Written by Lauren Holowaty

Printed by Rotolito in Romania

ACAMAR FILMS

Contents

Sledging Fun

Bing is zooming around in the snow on his Hoppity Rocket Sledge with his friends. Can you spot eight differences between the two pictures?

Colour in a Hoppity Rocket Sledge as you spot each difference.

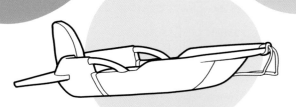

Answers: 1. Part of Bing's sledge has changed colour, 2. Bing is wearing a Santa hat, 3. Sula's gloves are now green, 4. A bird has appeared, 5. Nicky's boots are purple, 6. Flop has joined them, 7. One of Sula's buttons has vanished, 8. Bing's coat has changed colour

Snowman Style

Flop and Bing are making snowman decorations today. Help them make lots more by using your crayons to dress up these snowmen.

Don't forget to add eyes, a nose, a smile and something for each snowman to wear.

Special Delivery

Bing has made Sula a Christmas card. Help guide Flop and Bing from the start to the finish along the snowman stepping stones.

Remember, Flop and Bing can only step on the snowman stepping stones!

Kite

Round the corner, not far away,
Bing wants to fly his kite today . . .

Bing and Flop are in the park.

"I'm going to fly my **Hoppity Voosh kite!**" says Bing, holding the kite tube.

"Okay," says Flop. "You hold that end and I'll pull . . ."

"I can do it," says Bing, wanting to do it all by himself.

He turns the tube upside down and gives it a good shake, but the kite is stuck.

"It won't come out!"
says Bing.

"Why don't we do it together?" suggests Flop.

With Flop's help, Bing pulls the kite out . . .

. . . "Hello, Hoppity," Bing says to his kite. But Hoppity is all tied up.

"There, that's better," says Flop, untangling the string.

"Can I fly it now?" asks Bing.

"Yup," says Flop. "It's nice and breezy today. Great weather for kite flying!"

"Hoppity . . . Voooosh . . .!" Bing says, throwing his kite up into the air.

Whoops!

The kite flip-flaps down to the ground.

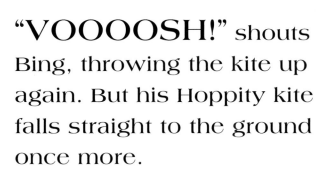

"VOOOOSH!" shouts Bing, throwing the kite up again. But his Hoppity kite falls straight to the ground once more.

Flop points across the park to some other kite flyers. "Why don't we see how they're doing it?" he suggests.

"Oh," says Bing, watching them. "They're running **really fast!**"

One of the kite flyers **throws** the kite up in the air and it **sails** on the wind. Bing **jumps** up and down excitedly . . .

"Voooosh! Wheeeeeee!"

"Up it goes," says Flop. "Up, up, up . . . Look at it, Bing!"

"I'm going to do that, Flop," says Bing.

"Okay," says Flop. "How about I hold the kite for you and you pull the string . . ."

Festive Food

Bing's friends are at his house for Christmas lunch. The table is nearly ready, but something's missing. Can you find the right puzzle piece to finish the picture?

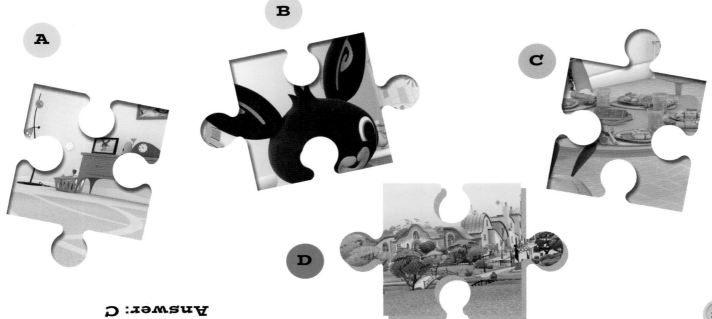

A

B

C

D

Answer: C

Beautiful Baubles

Ooh, sparkly! Look at the rows of lovely baubles from Bing's Christmas tree. Which bauble comes next in each row?

1

2

3

4

Answers: 1. 2. 3. 4.

Which bauble is your favourite?

26

Pretty Patterns

Decorate your own bauble to put on the tree.
Trace the shapes and colour them in.

Can you spot a triangle?

Which shape is a circle?

How many sides does a square have?

Christmas Colouring Game

Bing and Sula have Christmas presents for each other. Play this game to colour in their pictures.

1. Red
2. Green
3. Brown
4. Yellow
5. Blue
6. Black

28

How to play:

1. Find a friend to play with and choose a picture each.

2. Take it in turns to roll a dice and find the matching number on your picture to see which part to colour in.

3. Keep taking it in turns to roll and colour until one player has coloured in their whole picture.

1. Pink

2. Red

3. Yellow

4. Green

5. Blue

6. Brown

You could give your finished picture to a friend as a present!

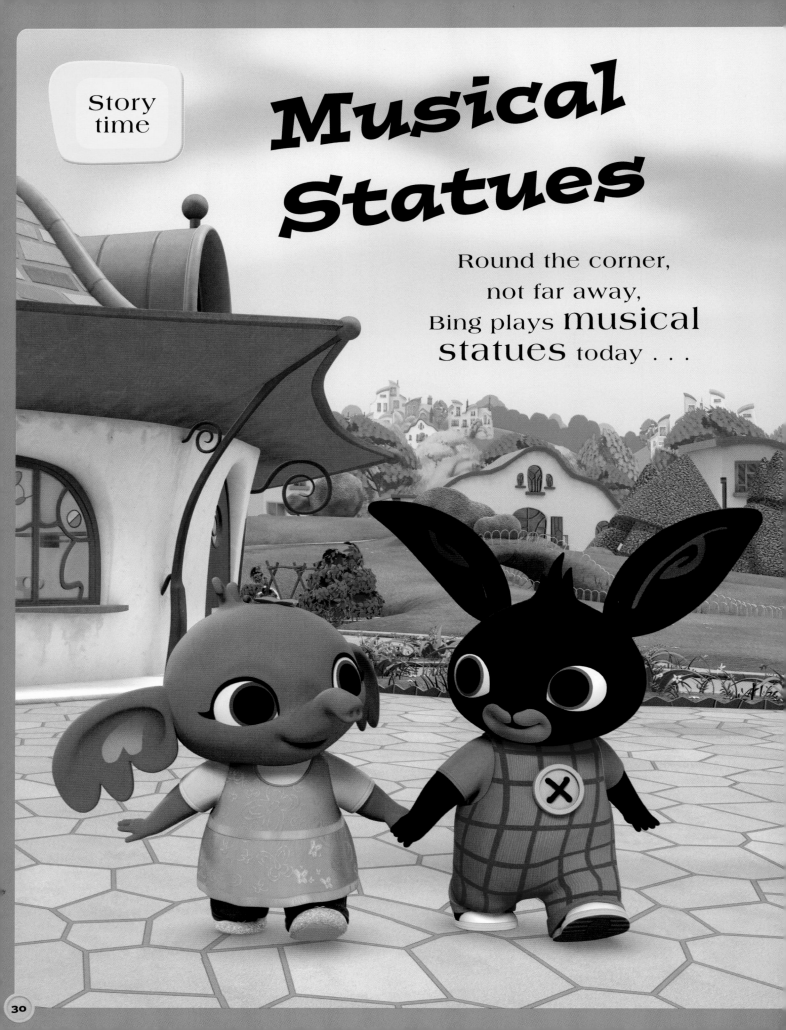

Musical Statues

Round the corner,
not far away,
Bing plays **musical
statues** today . . .

Bing is at Amma's crèche and wants to play musical statues.

"Do you all remember how to play?" asks Amma.

"You dance with the music," explains Bing. Flop shows them by putting music on and dancing.

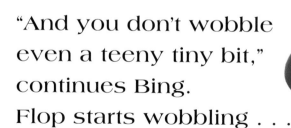

"Then the music stops and you stand statue-still," says Bing.

Flop stops dancing and stands still on one leg.

"And you don't wobble even a teeny tiny bit," continues Bing. Flop starts wobbling . . .

"You're OUT, Flop!" shouts Bing. "And now you're a wobble-watcher."

"And the last one left is the winner!" cheers Sula.

"Yes. Me!" says Bing. "I'm going to be the winner."

Flop starts the music, but it's too slow.

"It's not **dancy** enough, Flop," says Bing.

Flop tries another song, which is much faster.

"**Yesssss!**" cheer Bing, Coco, Sula and Pando as they all start dancing.

Suddenly the music stops and everyone is statue-still except for Pando.

"Pando, the music's stopped," says Sula. "You have to stop dancing or you're out."

"**Ohhh,**" says Pando.

They start the game again.

"Remember to **focus**," says Amma. "And when the music stops, stand statue-still."

The music starts, but Pando doesn't move.

"Pando," says Amma. "The music's started. **Dance!**"

Everyone jumps around until Flop stops the music and they all stand statue-still.

"I'm a **wobble-watcher**," says Amma walking around to see if anyone is moving.

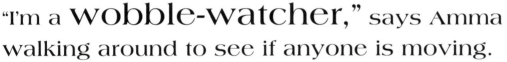

Charlie thinks it's very funny and starts giggling. Then Sula starts to giggle and **wobble**.

"You're out, Sula," says Amma. "Now you're a wobble-watcher too."

"Charlie made me laugh," says Sula. "He's out too."

Flop starts the music again.

"Oooh, I **love** this song!"
says Coco, spinning around.
Suddenly the music stops.

"You wobbled, Coco.
You're out!" says Sula.

"Ohhh, I couldn't
stop spinning,"
laughs Coco.

"Now **you're** a
wobble-watcher too
Coco," says Amma.

The music starts and Bing and Pando begin
dancing again, until Flop stops the music . . .
Bing and Pando stay **statue-still.**

"**We're** watching for **wobblers,**" sings Coco.

But no one wobbles!

Flop puts the music on again and Bing and Pando
start dancing.

This time, when the
music stops, Bing
is balancing on
one leg.

"Bing's going to
wobble,"
says Coco.

"Bing, you're
wobbling **all** over,"
says Sula.

Bing puts his leg down to stop wobbling.

"**Pando!**" says Amma. "You're the **last one**
standing statue-still."

"Ohhh," sighs Bing.

"**Woohoo!**"
cheers Pando.

"Well done,
everybody,"
says Amma.

"**Yaaaay!**" everyone cheers, except Bing.

Bing is upset that he didn't win and doesn't want to play any more. He wanders over to the sofa.

"I wanted to be the last one," Bing tells Flop. "I chose the game."

"Yup, and everybody loved it," says Flop.

"But I wanted to be the winner," says Bing.

"Well, maybe next time you'll be the winner," says Flop. "How about we go and try again?"

"Hmm . . . okay," says Bing.

Charlie comes over to see Bing.

"Bing-Bing-Bing-Bing-Bing,"

he says, laughing. It cheers Bing up.

"Charlie wants to play again too," says Bing.

"**Bing!** Dance with us!" says Sula.

Bing goes over to dance with everyone.

"**Woohoo!**" cheers Coco. "This time **I'm** going to be statue-still last."

"Or it might be me," says Bing. "I'm not going to wobble."

"Let's find out," says Amma.

Bing chooses a song that everybody likes and they all have lots of fun dancing together.

"**Yay!**"

Musical statues . . .
it's a **Bing thing.**

Musical Statues Story Quiz

Can you remember what happened in the story?
See if you can answer these questions.

1 Whose idea was it to play the musical statues game? Trace the letters of the right name.

A Sula

B Bing

C Pando

2 What do you have to do when the music stops?

A stand statue-still

B move

C sing

3 What was Bing doing when he wobbled? Point to the right answer.

A Standing on one leg

B Sitting down

C Shaking his arms in the air

4 What colour was the sofa Bing sat on? Use a crayon to colour in the correct answer.

A red

B yellow

C green

Answers: 1. B, 2. A, 3. A, 4. C

38

Statue-still Shadows

Playing musical statues was lots of fun! Can you help wobble-watch by drawing lines or pointing to everyone's matching statue-still shadows?

Answers: 1. B, 2. C, 3. D, 4. A

Make Some Noise!

You will need:
- a dice
- two small counters

Bing and his friends love making music! Find a friend and play Bing's noisy board game.

What to do:

1. Place your counters on the START.
2. The youngest player rolls the dice first.
3. Take it in turns to roll a dice and move around the board.
4. Wherever you land, make the sound of the musical instrument (Bang! Bang! Rattle! Shake! Plinky plonk!).
The first player to reach the FINISH and make all the noises is the winner!

START

7

8

6

5

16

17

1

4

18

2

3

40

9

10

11

12

15

14

13

FINISH

20

19

41

Let's Dance

It's time to dance! Join the dots to finish the picture of Bing and Sula dancing together. Then use your favourite crayons or colouring pencils to colour them in.

What songs
do you like to
dance to?

43

My Favourite Things

Bing has lots of favourite things! Here are some of them. Can you spot the matching pairs and draw a line between them?

1  A

2  B

3  C

4  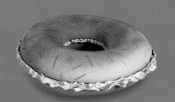 D

What are your favourite things?

Answers: 1. C, 2. D, 3. A, 4. B

Park Maze

Flop is helping Bing and Pando take it in turns on Pando's new skateboard. Use a pencil or your finger to trace a path for them through the park maze to Padget!

START

FINISH

45

Halloween Counting

It's Halloween and Bing, Sula, Flop and Amma are wearing fancy dress. Do you like their costumes? Look at the big picture and join in this counting game!

My wand is the most magical wand ever!

How many teeth does Bing's mask have?

6

How many shiny bells can you see on Flop's hat?

3

How many ghosts are there?

1

How many pumpkins are there?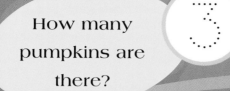

How many silver stripes can you count on Sula's unicorn horn?

And I'm the most bitey Biteysaurus ever!

How many green shoes can you spot? 2

What do you like to dress up as at Halloween?

47

Mitten's Kittens

Bing and Sula are playing with Mitten's kittens. Look at the small picture and use it to help you colour in the big one.

Have you ever stroked a kitten? How did they feel?

Biggest and Smallest

Amma has asked Bing and Sula to put some things in size order. Can you point to the biggest and smallest thing in each row?

1 A   B   C   D

2 A   B   C   D

3 A   B   C   D

4 A   B   C   D

Answers: 1. Biggest is D, smallest is A, 2. Biggest is C, smallest is D, 3. Biggest is A, smallest is C, 4. Biggest is B, smallest is D

49

Voosh!

Round the corner, not far away,
Bing is **voosh**ing Hoppity today . . .

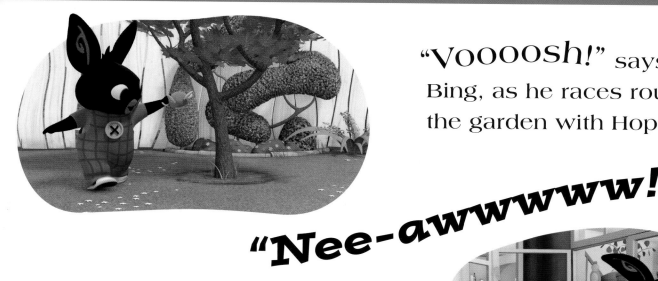

"VOOOOSH!" says Bing, as he races round the garden with Hoppity.

"Nee-awwwww!"

Flop brings the laundry basket out into the garden.

"Can I help hang up the washing?" asks Bing.

"Of course," says Flop. "Thank you, Bing."

Bing turns the handle to lower the washing line.

Crank! Crank!

"Here . . . we . . . go, go, go, go, **gOOOOO!**" cheer Bing and Flop together, as the washing line comes down.

Bing wants to do more helping so he passes a sock to Flop. Then he picks up a peg.

"**Woah,**" says Bing, squeezing the peg. "It's all **bitey.**"

Snap! Snap!

Bing snaps the peg on to the sock and hangs it on the washing line.

Snap!

"That's it," says Flop, as he hangs more washing on the line.

Bing shows Hoppity the washing. "Look! That's my red towel, Hoppity."
Bing sniffs his towel . . .

Sniffff!

"Mmm . . . it smells all nice and clean," Bing tells Hoppity, as he holds him up to smell the towel too. "Ohhh, lovely!" says Bing, in his Hoppity voice.

Flop raises the line up high . . .

Crank!

Crank!

"Flop!" calls Bing. "Me and Hoppity didn't say hello to **my pants.**"

"Oh," says Flop.

Bing throws Hoppity **high** into the air, up towards his pants . . .

"Hoppity Voooosh!

Hello, pants," says Bing. "Why do you put them **up, up, up,** Flop?" he says, pointing to the washing line.

"Well, the wind is stronger up, up, up, Bing," says Flop. "And the wind is quick at **whooshing** clothes dry."

"Look, Flop!" says Bing, holding his arms out. **"I'm the wind . . .**

Whoo-oooo-ooooosh!"

Bing spins round and round, whooshing like the wind.

"Hoppity Voooooosh!"

Bing slips and Hoppity **flies** out of his hand and through the air.

"**Oh!**" cries Bing, as he lands with a bump on his bottom.

"You okay, Bing?" Flop asks.

"Yup," replies Bing. Then he looks around. "Where's Hoppity?" he asks.

"Let's see," says Flop.

"He went up," says Bing, pointing up into the air. "**Really** high."

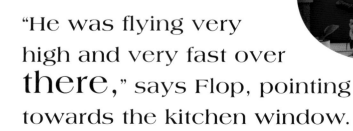

"He was flying very high and very fast over **there,**" says Flop, pointing towards the kitchen window.

"Ohhh," says Bing.

"Hoppity!" calls Bing, running into the house. "Where are you, Hoppity?" Bing crawls under the table. "I can't see him, Flop," he says.

"Well, let's think," says Flop. "Where did he come from?"

"Err," says Bing, thinking. "He flew in the window." Bing races over to the open window . . .

"Hoppity! Ohhh!" says Bing, as he spots Hoppity in the dirty water.

"Oh, Flop," says Bing sadly, pulling Hoppity out of the sink. "Hoppity's all **dirty** and **drippy**."

"Don't worry, Bing," says Flop. "It's **no big thing.** We just need to give Hoppity a wash."

"Not in the washing machine," says Bing, hugging Hoppity. "He won't like that. It's too spinny."

Flop suggests they give Hoppity a bath with Bubble Duck in the sink.

Sploosh!

Bing puts Hoppity into the warm, bubbly water and pulls him out.

"Look, Flop!" says Bing. "Hoppity's got a **bubble hat!**"

Bing wraps Hoppity
in a cloth to dry him.

Chkkka-chkkka!

"He's still wet, Flop,"
says Bing.

Suddenly he has an idea. "Ohhh! The **wind!**
The wind can **whooooosh** Hoppity dry."

"Good idea, Bing," says Flop.

Bing is worried that Hoppity
won't like the bitey pegs.

"Hoppity doesn't **need**
pegs," says Flop, pointing.

"Ahhh, Hoppity can **voosh** up
in my pants!" says Bing.

"Hoppity Voooooosh!"

cheer Flop and Bing, as Flop
raises the washing line.

"Now he can get all dry in the wind," says Bing.

"Good for you, Bing bunny!"
says Flop.

Voooooshing . . .
it's a **Bing thing.**

Voosh! Story Quiz

Think back to the story. What can you remember about it?

1 Colour in the toy Bing was playing with in the story.

A
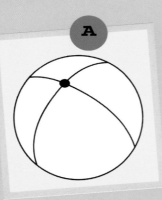

B

C

2 Where did Bing's toy land when it flew through the window? Point to the right answer.

A
On a
chair

B
Under the
table

C
In the
sink

3 What did Bing use to make Hoppity's bath all bubbly? Tick the right answer.

A
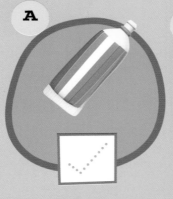

B
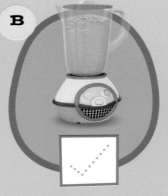

C
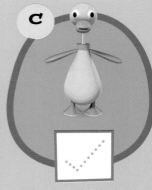

4 What did Bing put Hoppity in on the washing line? Colour in the peg next to the right item of clothing.

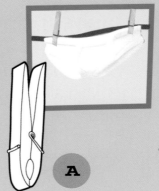

A   **B**   **C**

Answers: 1. B, 2. C, 3. C, 4. A

Where's Fairy Hippo?

Voooooosh! Follow the tangled lines to help Sula find Fairy Hippo. Which way did she fly?

Time for a Hug

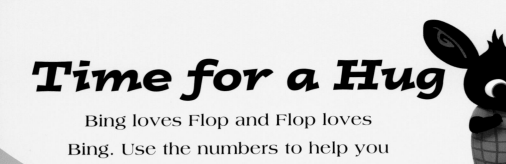

Bing loves Flop and Flop loves Bing. Use the numbers to help you colour in the picture.

1. Black

2. Green

3. Red

4. Orange

5. Brown

Up or Down?

Hoppity went **voooosh**, high up into the air and then came down again. Look at the pictures of Hoppity. Is he **up** in the air or **down** on the ground in each one?

1

2

3

4

Answers: 1. Up, 2. Down, 3. Up, 4. Down

Bouncy Balloons

Bing and his friends love bouncy balloons! How many of each coloured balloon can you spot? Count them up, then trace over the dotty number on the balloon!

Which colour balloon is there the most of?

Answer: There are more green balloons than other colours.

65

Helping Hand

Bing is helping to tidy up. Can you help tidy too?
Point to or circle the odd one out in each group,
so they can be tidied away.

Answers: 1. 2. 3. 4.

Bing's Bedtime Story

Bing is tucked up in bed ready for Flop to read him a story.
Spend a few minutes looking at this picture.

Now turn the
page and see
what you can
remember.

Memory Quiz

What can you remember about the
picture on the previous page?

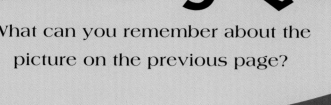

1

Where was
Bing in the
picture?

2

What was
Bing holding
in his hand?

 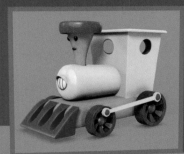 

3

Who was
sitting next to
Bing?

4

What was on
Bing's bedside
table?

Answers: 1. In bed, 2. Hoppity, 3. Flop, 4. Owly

We've got story time covered! This entertaining collection of books follow Bing and his friends as they explore the world around them! We have plenty of titles to choose from, which can be enjoyed again and again!

DON'T MISS!

Sula's Shop

Bing's Bus Ride

Merry Christmas, Bing!

Bing's New Friend

My First Little Library

Where's Bing?
A lift-the-flap book

My Toilet Train Sticker Book

With over 75 stickers and a reward chart!

Toilet-training fun for boys and girls

The Rainybow Song

Press the button Sing the song

Fun at the Park! Magnet Book